LOOK AND FIND

ANIMANIACS

Illustrated by
Jaime Diaz Studios

Illustration Script Development by
Neal Sternecky

Published by Louis Weber, C.E.O.
Publications International, Ltd.
7373 North Cicero Avenue
Lincolnwood, Illinois 60646

© 1994 Warner Bros.

Manufactured in the U.S.A.

8 7 6 5 4 3 2 1

ISBN: 0-7853-0698-6

PUBLICATIONS INTERNATIONAL, LTD.

It's a busy day at the movie studio, and we Warners have a busy day of our own planned. The Hip Hippos are throwing a party, so we're sneaking out ASAP! And speaking of a sap, Ralph the Guard is on duty, so a clean getaway will be a breeze! Did I say breeze? Answer correctly and win ten million dollars! Just kidding. See if you can find these breezy, windy, gale-force, blowhard things on the studio lot.

An electric fan

A kite

A weather vane

A sailboat

A paper airplane

A windmill

Wakko's underwear

The CEO (he's full of hot air)

While strolling through the park that day, we ran into Rita and Runt. After we helped them up and said we were sorry, they asked us to help them find a home—any home. They were desperate! Desperate, they said! We found a BUNCH of perfectly good homes for them, and they turned their cold, wet noses up at every one of them! There's just no pleasing some people! Go fig! Can you find these cozy little places we uncovered for those two vagabonds?

A pup tent

A houseboat

An outhouse

A doghouse

An igloo

A tree house

A log cabin

A greenhouse

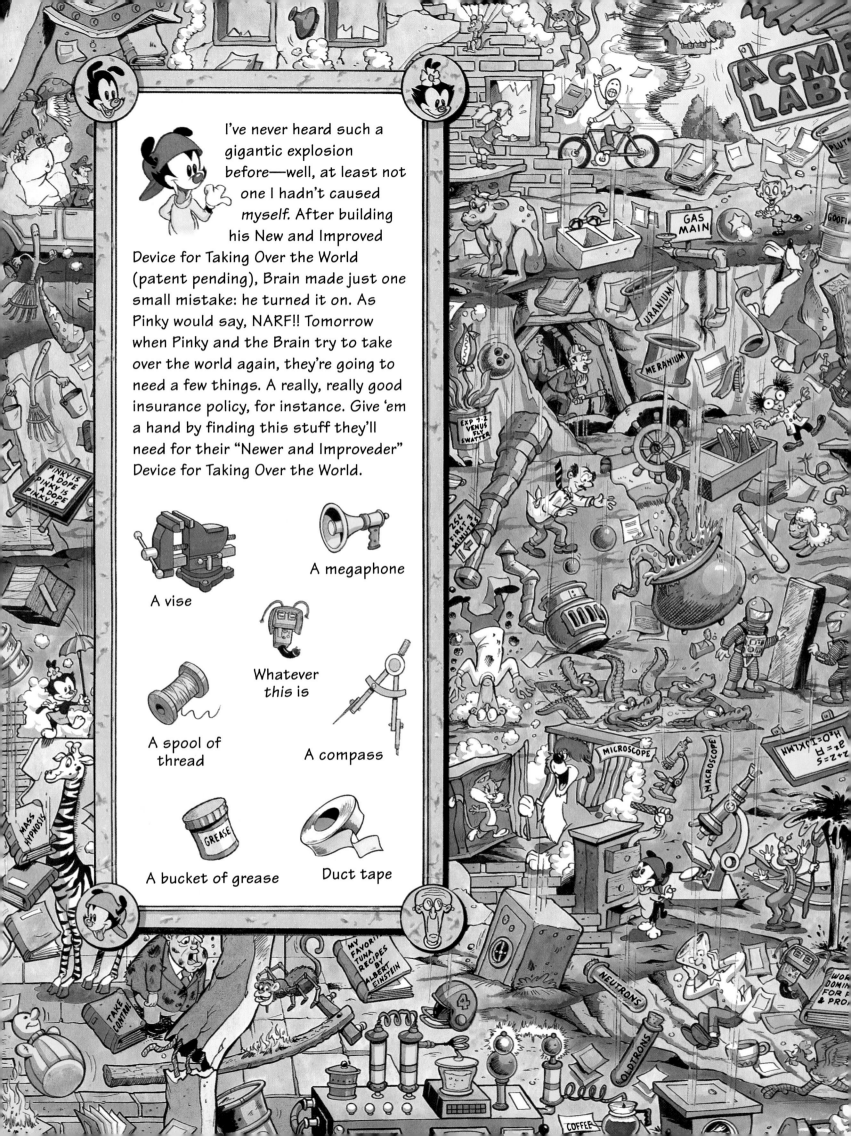

I've never heard such a gigantic explosion before—well, at least not one I hadn't caused myself. After building his New and Improved Device for Taking Over the World (patent pending), Brain made just one small mistake: he turned it on. As Pinky would say, NARF!! Tomorrow when Pinky and the Brain try to take over the world again, they're going to need a few things. A really, really good insurance policy, for instance. Give 'em a hand by finding this stuff they'll need for their "Newer and Improveder" Device for Taking Over the World.

A vise

A megaphone

Whatever this is

A spool of thread

A compass

A bucket of grease

Duct tape

We figured Ditzyland would be a good spot to ditch Ralph, The Nurse, and Scratchansniff on our way to the Hippos' party. Besides, everyone who enters the park gets one of those complimentary Ditzy Dawg beanies that are just too, too— YEEEUCKKK! Even Buttons got one, and he's just here to rescue Mindy— from herself. What a cute kid. She kind of reminds me of me! Have a look around and see if you can find me and these other characters at the park. Okay, I love you, bye-bye. (See, Mindy's got nothin' on me.)

Yakko

Ditzy Dawg

Buttons

Wakko

Bingo Bunny

Mindy

Dot

Pixilated Pig

When Wakko found out about the Hippos' party, I told him to keep it under his hat. That got me thinking about what else might be under that red baseball cap, so I decided to look inside Wakko's brain—to explore deranged new worlds, to seek out new laughs and new insubordination, to boldly go where no sense has gone before! Pretty exciting stuff, huh? It turns out that, contrary to popular belief, Wakko hasn't lost his mind. He's just misplaced some of the things that make other people so . . . boring. See if you can dig up these items that are scarce in Wakko's noggin.

Manners

Snobbery

Selfishness

Worries

Self-control

A conventional idea

STEPJAZZEROBISTAIRICIZE ~ DRIVE THRU

We're on our way to the Hip Hippos' party, but we just had to stop by and help our friend Slappy the Squirrel celebrate her big night. She's leaving her pawprints in cement here at Growlmann's Chinese Theater. Slappy said the last time she had an honor like this was in a ceremony with Sergeant O'Malley at the Third Precinct, and it took two days to get the ink off her fingers. (Now that's comedy!) Anyway, the place is packed with cartoon stars. See if you can find these animated celebrities.

The Pink Puma

Sloppy Doo

Slappy the Squirrel

Skippy

Stoney the Chipmunk

Beany the Bison

Sid the Squid

Walter Wolf

We had some free time before the party, so we said to ourselves, "Ourselves, let's call on some of that reliable Warner spontaneity and head to New York for a visit with our fine fettered friends, the Goodfeathers!" The Big Apple is just lovely this time of year, and besides, their contract says they get to appear in all the merchandise. As long as you're here with us, don't just sit there laughing; help Bobby, Pesto, and Squit find these snacks or they'll peck ya' 'til Tuesday.

A hot dog

A pepperoni pizza

A spilled soda

A soft pretzel

A taffy apple

A bag of peanuts

A Porterhouse steak

We flew back in from New York—and boy, were our arms tired—just in time to be fashionably late for the Hippos' swingin' party. Then we realized that we didn't have our invitations with us—mostly because we hadn't actually been invited. But of course that didn't stop us! Do we know how to crash a party or what? Now that we're here, why don't you see if you can find some of the more stuffy, boring, pompous guests, and that way I can be sure to stay away from them!

The Bigshot Director

Pip Pumphandle

General Miswith Grapeshot

The CEO

Trent Setter

Biff Mogulson

Dame Pruda Kramweed

The security guards on the movie lot will use anything they can to catch the Warner brothers and their sister Dot. See if you can find these traps.

- ☐ Butterfly net
- ☐ Cage
- ☐ Mousetrap
- ☐ "Sand" trap
- ☐ Ice cream trap
- ☐ Trapdoor
- ☐ Trapeze

In the park, the Warners only compounded Rita and Runt's problems. Can you find these compound words?

- ☐ Shoe tree
- ☐ Flower girl
- ☐ Cameraman
- ☐ Sunflower
- ☐ Doorman
- ☐ Egghead
- ☐ Sheepdog
- ☐ Car pool

The scientists at the Acme Lab have cooked up some strange animals. Go back there and find these weird creatures if you dare!

- ☐ Bullfrog
- ☐ Catfish
- ☐ Bird dog
- ☐ Turtle dove
- ☐ Ant farmer
- ☐ Spider monkey
- ☐ Sea lion
- ☐ Sheepdog

You just finished this book! What are you going to do next? Why not go to Ditzyland and find these souvenirs?

- ☐ A Ditzyland pennant
- ☐ A Ditzyland T-shirt
- ☐ A Ditzyland jackhammer
- ☐ A Ditzyland sailboat
- ☐ Ditzyland home tattoo kits
- ☐ A Ditzyland tractor
- ☐ A Ditzyland washing machine
- ☐ Ditzyland lawn ornaments